D1551171

FINDING YOUR SPOT IN THE WORLD

A STORY ABOUT DIVERSITY

Written & Illustrated
by Diane Alber

To my children, Ryan and Anna:
You both have a special SPOT in this world and
in my heart!

Copyright © 2020 Diane Alber
All Rights Reserved
All inquiries about this book can be sent to the author at
info@dianealber.com
Published in the United States by Diane Alber Art LLC
ISBN: For more information, or to book an event, visit our website:
ISBN 978-1-951287-18-4
www.dianealber.com
Paperback
Printed in China

This book belongs to:

_____

_____

_____

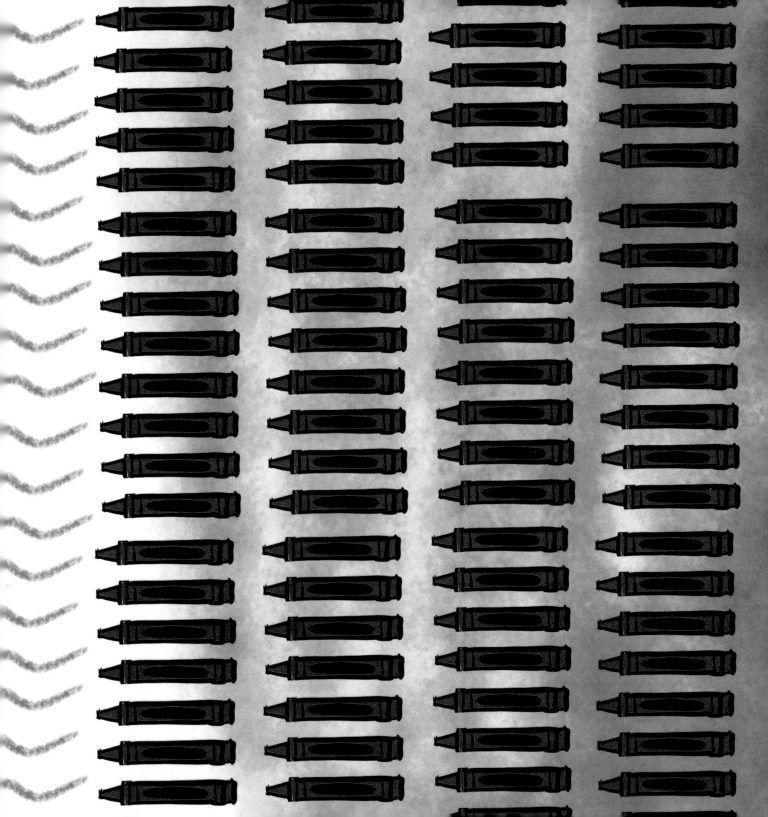

Being different comes in all shapes and sizes. Some differences you can see and some differences you can't.

You may see someone move differently, **but we all want to go places and explore!**

(You can download this page on my website for FREE at www.dianealber.com)

CAN YOU SPT WHAT MAKES YOU UNIQUE?

SELF PORTRAIT

I am good at ———————

I like to eat ———————

I like to watch ——————

I like to play ——————

I want to be ———————

I like to listen to ——————

Added Learning: What does diversity mean?
Do you think diversity is important? Why or why not?
What drawings would we miss out coloring if we only had red crayons?
Name one time you learned from someone who was different than you?
Name one way our differences can make the world better?

Made in the USA
Coppell, TX
26 May 2020

26501681R00021